OLD BRITISH LIVESTOCK

John Vince

Shire Publications Ltd.

CONTENTS

The opinions expressed in this book are the author's and do not represent the views of any other organisation.

INTRODUCTION

We have become accustomed in recent years to appeals to preserve buildings or machines which have a special historic or aesthetic value. Now whole groups of buildings may be designated as conservation areas to prevent their alteration or demolition and it would be easy to conclude that all historic things shared such common static qualities. There is one important part of our British history, however, which has never stood still.

The farmer's livestock has its own fascinating tale to tell. Once there were dozens of local breeds of cattle, sheep and pigs. In the eighteenth century breeders started to experiment with improved breeds in a scientific manner, and from their labours most of our modern stock was developed.

But some breeds remain unchanged, like the Soay sheep, whose ancestors wandered about Europe in prehistoric days. The descendants of the sheep carried aboard Viking longships are still to be seen and Portland sheep are claimed to date from the Armada. For all those who can appreciate and enjoy the living past, there is an amazing amount of British history still trotting around on four legs.

Unfortunately, many of our ancient breeds, like the Sheeted Somerset cattle, have disappeared and can only be found among the pages of agricultural text books. Some of the breeds shown in this book now exist in very small numbers and their survival will depend very largely on the work of the Rare Breed Survival Trust and its enthusiastic members. Public support for farm parks will materially assist the efforts of those who aim to keep our living history on the move. Some farm parks and societies are listed at the end of this book.

DRAUGHT HORSES

In the last century three principal breeds of farmhorse dominated the agricultural scene: the Shires, the Clydesdales and the Suffolks, their distinctive characteristics evolved over a long period of time. Apart from these three well-defined breeds there must have been hundreds of cross-bred variations. It seems unlikely that our English horses have exclusively island blood in their veins. An early importation of foreign horse flesh to these shores is shown in the Bayeux Tapestry: William the Conqueror brought his own war horses. A thousand years earlier the Romans had done the same. Later, the war horse developed and the fifteenth-century manuscript in the British Museum (Cott. MS Julius E IV) which depicts the life of Richard Beauchamp, Earl of Warwick, has several good drawings of the war horses of the period. It is generally accepted that the heavy proportions of the Shires are derived from the breed which carried our monarchs into battle.

Not so long ago it seemed that the farmhorse was going to be completely replaced by the tractor. But the patient horse can still be useful when the tractor's tank runs dry. The fact that there are still breeders of heavy horses is largely due to the enthusiasm of the horse societies listed at the end of this book. The working horse which was once thought to be obsolete may again emerge to help rescue the nation's for-

A magnificently attired pair of Shire horses.

Ploughing with a pair of Clydesdales.

tunes, as it did in 1939. In recent years societies like the Southern Counties Horse Ploughing Association have contributed to the revival of this skill.

SHIRES

OPPOSITE: Lineal descendants of ancient war horses, this pair is magnificently attired for a ploughing match. A turn-out like this was commonplace in the Victorian farmer's calendar. Apart from the prize money, the ploughing match gave the ploughman an opportunity to display his skill to his neighbours. In 1884 breeders of Shire horses were advised to breed stock as large as possible. One reason for this advice was the demand which then existed in large towns like Liverpool for single horses which could manage a heavy load unaided. In the crowded streets of the time it was 'far more convenient to use one horse that can move several tons, than some two or three, which take up so much room'. The Shire stud book traces the ancestry of the breed back to 1770. Distant ancestors were black but in modern times bay, brown, grey, roan or chestnut have widened the spectrum.

CLYDESDALES

ABOVE: The remote medieval ancestors of the Clydesdales and the Shires probably had enough characteristics in common to allow us to accept that they shared the same family tree. Early in the eighteenth century John Paterson of Lochlyoch introduced Flemish blood into the emerging breed. They began to dominate the horse world north of the Border and all the desirable characteristics of the local regional types were combined in the Clydesdale's endurance, strength and hardiness. Dark brown and dappled were the most popular colours a century ago; grey and bay were looked upon with disfavour.

5

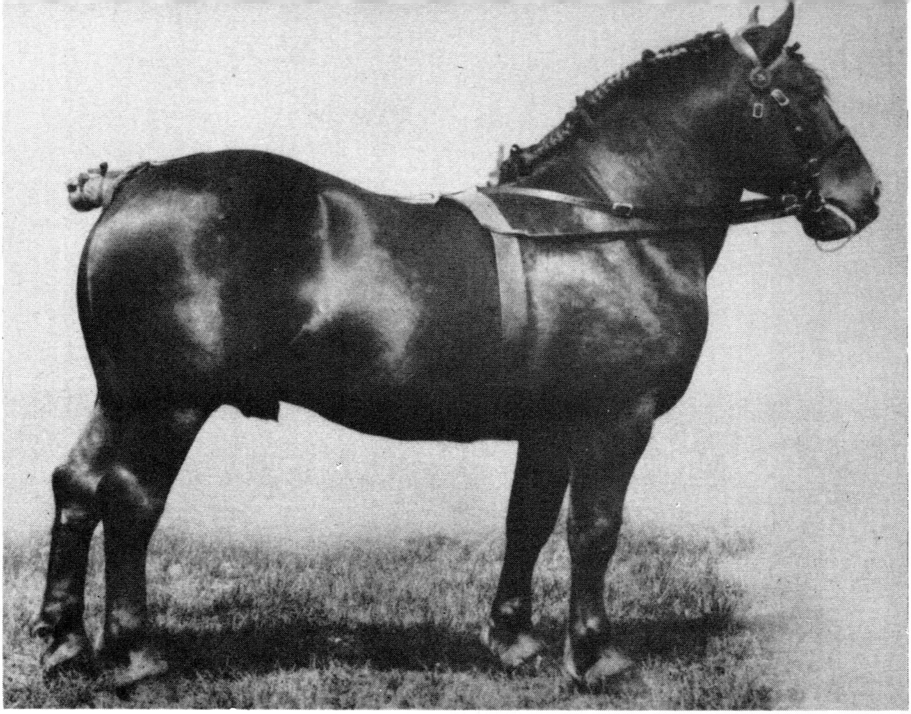

SUFFOLKS

ABOVE: This compact and most powerful of our native breeds originated in the county which provided its name in the early sixteenth century. As far as the written record is concerned all the registered Suffolks can be traced back to 1768, when in the village of Ufford the stallion called Crisp's Horse was born. It became the modern ancestor of the Suffolks. They do not display the variety of colours found in the other breeds.

PERCHERONS

BELOW: These horses take their name from Le Perche in north-west France. Percherons were to be found in Britain in late Victorian times when they were the favoured draught animals for London omnibuses. The British Percheron Horse Society was formed in 1918. Percherons are black, grey or dappled. These, photographed at the Southern Counties Horse Ploughing Association Match in 1973.

CATTLE

The development of British cattle breeds was the result of several influences which originated in the eighteenth century. As the population increased and towns began to expand new demands were made upon farmers. The change from self-sufficient village communities with regulated seasonal habits to the hungry and incessant demands of the new towns took place slowly, but the farmer had to respond even if it meant discarding the methods revered by his ancestors. New fodder crops made it possible to winter cattle instead of slaughtering them. In this way more good beasts survived from which to breed. Pioneers like Robert Bakewell, Charles and Robert Colling made important advances in cattle breeding, based on new scientific ideas. Knowledge of these improvements was spread through the printed word—particularly by Arthur Young (1741-1820), an agricultural journalist and secretary of the Board of Agriculture.

In this century, the demand for leaner meat has had its effect on the methods of meat production, and the older stock was readily discarded in favour of new crossbreds. However, farsighted men saw the need to preserve adequate stocks of older breeds which, though not economic propositions at present, may possess irreplaceable genetic qualities. Science has made it possible to establish gene banks which can provide future breeders with essential genetic elements.

Breeders gave cattle different names at each stage of development. At birth the male was called a bull calf (bullock calf if castrated). It then became a year-old bull (or stott if castrated). Stotts became steers, bullocks or oxen. The female calf was called a cow calf, heifer calf or quey calf. The terms quey or heifer were used until the first calf was born when the heifer became a cow.

SHORTHORNS: This important breed probably has its ancestry in the aboriginal cattle of the north-eastern corner of England. The modern strain can be attributed to Robert and Charles Colling who farmed at Ketton, Darlington, in the eighteenth century. Charles was a pupil of the famous Robert Bakewell (1725-95) of Leicester. Robert and Charles Colling established their Shorthorn herd with a single bull, noticed near the church at Houghton-le-Skerne, and four selected cows. The brothers discovered that by special breeding it was possible to establish fixed characteristics in a herd. Precise details of their breeding methods are not known but their success indicates that they were able to avoid the hazards which in-breeding can produce. In the early years of the nineteenth century their cows and bulls fetched as much as £100 — a fantastic figure at that time. The Collings' herds were eventually sold in 1810 and 1818. At Charles Colling's sale at Ketton the eighteen bulls established an average of £169 8s. 0d. each. The real sensation of the sale was a price of a thousand guineas paid for the bull 'Cornet'. Robert's sale, at Barmpton, took place at a time of relative depression just after the end of the Napoleonic Wars, but his herd of sixty-one realised an average price of £128 9s. 10d.

Although the Colling brothers can claim to be the founders of the breed we should note certain of their successors. At the Ketton sale Thomas Bates bought the heifer 'Old Duchess' for 183 guineas. Thomas Booth purchased the bull 'Albion' for 60 guineas. In 1818 John Booth acquired the yearling bull 'Pilot' for 270 guineas. From that time onwards two important strains of Shorthorn were developed. The names of Bates and Booth have an honourable place in the history of the Shorthorn breed which also contains many other variations.

HEREFORDS: This breed takes its name from the region in which it originated. As early as 1766 Benjamin Tompkins began to improve the breed in a systematic manner. Its native characteristics may have been added to at distant times by cattle from Europe but the dominant features are thought to be indigenous. One of the distinctive features of the Hereford — its white face — may in fact reflect the introduction of European blood. In the last century grey-faced or spotted-faced animals

BELOW: *A shorthorn cow c.1890. Notice the more rectangular body and shorter legs than in the earlier illustration (page 7).*

were not uncommon, and one strain was known as the 'Smoky-faced Montgomerys'.

DEVON CATTLE: The remoteness of the western counties and the difficulty of travelling helped to isolate Somerset, Devon and Cornwall two centuries or so ago. The aboriginal cattle matured in relative isolation from other breeds and there was probably no cross breeding of any importance. For hundreds of years the breed held sway over Devon and neighbouring Somerset. That inveterate traveller Andrew Young gathered details of the Devon herds for his report on the state of the county's agriculture. He mentions particularly the Quartly herd at Molland — where Mr Quartly and his brother 'the clergyman who interests himself much in live stock' were to be found. In Molland church there is a public notice issued at the time when an invasion by Napoleon was expected. The order must have caused Henry Quartly considerable anxiety. It directed that all stock should be slaughtered if the community was taken unawares; otherwise the cattle had to be driven into Somerset or to Dartmoor. There were two principal strains of Devons — the North Devons and the South Devons or Hams The latter strain was larger and provided more milk. According to Victorian writers there was a significant amount of Devon blood in the old Sussex breed.

ABOVE: *A nineteenth-century engraving of a Devon bull.*

KYLOES-WEST HIGHLAND CATTLE: The long coats and spreading horns of the Highland cattle make them particularly attractive creatures. Their origin in the cold northern corner of the British Isles has made them the hardiest of our native breeds. They can exist on the exposed moorland grazing which other breeds could not endure. Their milk is small in quantity but very rich. The principal value lies in their meat. Bullocks take three or four years to mature. Black was the dominant colour in Victorian days but brown, brindled, grey or dun were also common.

KERRYS: The mountains of Kerry have given their name to the only pure Irish breed. They are the best representation of aboriginal cattle to be found in Northern Europe and are distinguished by their diminutive size. Although they are the smallest breed they are hardy and adaptable. They were useful animals from the smallholder's point of view but were like the Kyloes, slow to mature. One Victorian writer's opinion of them is worth recording. Youatt said the Kerry was 'Truly the poor man's cow, living everwhere, hardy, yielding for her size abundance of milk of good quality, and fattening rapidly when required'.

DEXTER-KERRYS: An important branch of the Kerry breed was established 1830-1840 by a Mr Dexter. The Dexter-Kerry is shorter in the leg and plumper in the body. It is less elegant but more symmetrical than the Kerry.

LONGHORNS-CRAVENS: This breed has a particular historical importance. Robert Bakewell began his experiments with the Longhorns in 1755. Late in Victoria's reign the breed was considered to be in decline as other breeds had overtaken it in terms of profitability. As one Victorian writer remarked 'Although we look upon them with a kindly historic interest, it must now be reluctantly admitted that there is little reason for their continued existence.' The Longhorns are the largest cattle found among British breeds. A century or so ago they were to be found in Derby, Leicester, Warwick and the Craven district in Yorkshire — hence their alternative name.

ABOVE: *Kyloes-West Highland cattle are the hardiest of native British breeds.*

OPPOSITE TOP: *Dexter-Kerrys are shorter-legged than the Kerry breed.*

OPPOSITE BOTTOM: *Longhorn-Craven bull, cow and calf. Longhorn-Craven cattle are the largest amongst British breeds.*

POLLED ABERDEEN ANGUS: This hornless breed originated in Angus and Buchan where they were also known respectively as 'Doddies' and 'Humlies'. Competition from the Shorthorns inspired some significant improvements in this breed during the latter half of the last century.

AYRSHIRE: This breed had a reputation among Victorian farmers as a good milker. They were often crossed with advantage with Shorthorns. Little is known about the origins of the breed and it seems probable that some of its characteristics were derived from Dutch stock. It was an established breed in south-west Scotland early in the last century. In the 1960s it was to be found in Ayr, Lanark, Renfrew and Dunbarton. At that time it was beginning to replace the Galloways in Dumfries and in Galloway itself.

GALLOWAYS: This breed takes its name from the area in which it had its origin. It was recognised by the Victorians as an ancient breed with an established history of several centuries. At one time Galloways were the only cattle to be found in the south-west corner of Scotland i.e.

in Galloway, Kirkcudbright and Wigtown. In earlier days they had been prominent in Dumfries, Ayr, Renfrew and Lanark. In latter days the breed suffered from the growing popularity of the Ayrshire and, of course, the Shorthorn.

BELTED GALLOWAY: The Belted Galloway is now the only belted breed in Britain. Its distinctive characteristic is said to derive from the blood of the Dutch Lakenvelder which was introduced as long ago as the seventeenth century. Two other now extinct breeds which were known to contain belted (or sheeted) strains were the Suffolk Dun and the Sheeted Somerset. In 1934 the last herd of English Sheeted Cattle (from Romsey, Hants) was slaughtered as it failed to pass the tuberculin test. The Welsh Blacks still provide us with some belted animals even though a belted bull has not been used for more than a century.

JERSEYS: This breed is well known for the quality of its milk yield. Victorian gentlemen farmers favoured the Jersey as a decorative as well as a productive animal. Their sandy colour and deer-like heads made them particularly

attractive additions to parklands. An old name for this breed is Alderney. This latter breed seems to have once been a separate strain — being darker in colour — but it gradually became identified with the Jersey. Some suggest that there is a measure of Spanish blood to be found in the Jersey stock. Old pictures of Jersey bulls convey very clearly their definite 'Spanish' characteristics. A separate herd book for English Jerseys was established late in the last century.

GUERNSEYS: This larger and less elegant version of the Jersey breed originated in the islands of Guernsey, Alderney, Sark and Herm. Care was taken not to cross them with the Jerseys. The strong resemblance between Guernseys and the cattle of Normandy suggests that they share a common ancestry. From the early 1800s the islands of Jersey and Guernsey both enforced strict laws regarding the importation of cattle. None could enter for breeding purposes and no live animals at all were allowed to land from France. Careful records were kept of all English cattle admitted and they had to be slaughtered within ten weeks of their arrival. Even Guernsey cattle could not be re-admitted and special arrangements had to be made for animals taken to the mainland for showing purposes. The latter, subject to strict rules, were allowed to return. In this way the purity of the Channel Island herds was sustained.

RED POLLS: The generally accepted opinion is that Red Polls originated from crossing the native Norfolk and Suffolk breeds with Galloways from Scotland. Each resulting breed had its own distinct characteristics. The two strains, which probably date from late in the eighteenth century, were amalgamated in 1846. Several more years elapsed before the breed was given a name — Norfolk and Suffolk Polled — in 1862. Twenty years later the name was changed again to Red Polled.

WILD CATTLE: In the early nineteenth century there were about a dozen herds of wild cattle in various parts of Britain. By the 1890s these had been reduced to five: Chillingham (Northumberland), Cadzow (Hamilton), Vaynol Park (Bangor), Somerford (Cheshire) and Chartley (Staffs.). The Vaynol herd was moved there from Kilmory (Argyll) in 1886. These herds, which included horned and polled cattle, were the descendants of the wild cattle which had roamed the countryside in prehistoric times. The Victorian expert, Professor McKenny Hughes, considered that they derived from *Bos longifrons* (the Celtic Ox) which was about as big as a Kerry. These he thought had been crossed with Roman stock and their progeny in turn crossed again during the medieval period with cattle from the Low Countries.

GLOUCESTER CATTLE: The origin of this breed is obscure. Robert Trow-Smith suggested that it is derived from the stock once found in the Vale of Taunton Deane and among the lush meadows of Wiltshire, still renowned dairy country. The characteristic markings of the Gloucester are a dark red (brown) coat with finching, a white streak, along the line of the spine.

BELOW: *Gloucester cow and calves. The main colour of the coat is a dark reddish-brown.*

A Hereford-Shorthorn cross.

Many of the breeds mentioned above form an important part of our contemporary livestock. The changing demands of the market, however, compel the cattle breeder to look for new bloodstock in order to produce an adequate economic return for his labours, and such names as Charolais (from France), Chianina (from Italy) and Simmental (from Switzerland or Germany) now appear among the lists of better known breeds. Such breeds are crossed with native strains, and their progeny will come to be accepted as British.

ABOVE: *A Shorthorn. Compare the nineteenth-century engravings of this breed on pages 7 and 8.*

BELOW: *Southdown sheep.*
OPPOSITE: *A Jacob ram: also known as Spanish sheep from their country of origin.*

SHEEP

Many people have a romantic idea about the pastoral delights of shepherding, but for the shepherd there was little romance in digging ewes out of deep January snows. For the farmer sheep made an important contribution to the annual budget and they were looked upon very often as animals which paid the rent. Shepherds were concerned with raising the maximum number of lambs and had to count their flocks frequently to make sure none had strayed. In the north around the Border the old Gaelic numbers used by the shepherds survived into the twentieth century. They are not without interest and are recorded below.

One	—	yan
two	—	tyan
three	—	tethera
four	—	methera
five	—	pimp
six	—	sethera
seven	—	lethera
eight	—	hovera
nine	—	dovera
ten	—	dick
eleven	—	yan-a-dick
twelve	—	tyan-a-dick
thirteen	—	tethera-dick
fourteen	—	methera-dick
fifteen	—	bumfit
sixteen	—	yan-a-bumfit
seventeen	—	tyan-a-bumfit
eighteen	—	tethera-bumfit
nineteen	—	methera-bumfit
twenty	—	giggot

In common with all other work shepherding had its own jargon, which had many local variations. Male lambs were known as tups until they were weaned when they became tup hoggs, hoggets or teggs if castrated. After the first shearing they were known as tup shearlings, diamond tups, shearling wethers or dinmonts. The ewe lamb was also called a chilver in

ABOVE: *A Leicester sheep, once the most widely distributed breed.*

ABOVE: *Lincolns were renowned for the great weight of their wool.*

some areas. After weaning the term ewe hogg was used. From first to second clip (shearing) ewes were known as gimmers or threaves. A ewe not in lamb was called a barren gimmer or a yeld gimmer if not tupped. Another name used for sheep after first shear was quinter. Ewes not in lamb at the proper time were known as guessed ewes. Hand reared lambs also had special names. They were called cade lambs or tiddlin lambs (in Wilts/Glos). The inferior lambs in a flock were the pallies. Rejected ewes were the culls or shots. The draught ewes were those kept to lamb next season.

If a sheep rolled on to its back and could not get up it was said to be cast, awelled or rigwelted. After the shearing each sheep was marked with tar laid on with a buisting iron. Then the flock could return to the ewe haze or pasture.

The sheep raised by our ancestors provided the wealth that built the fine houses and 'wool' churches of East Anglia and the Cotswolds.

BELOW: *Cotswold sheep are probably descended from sheep introduced in Roman times.*

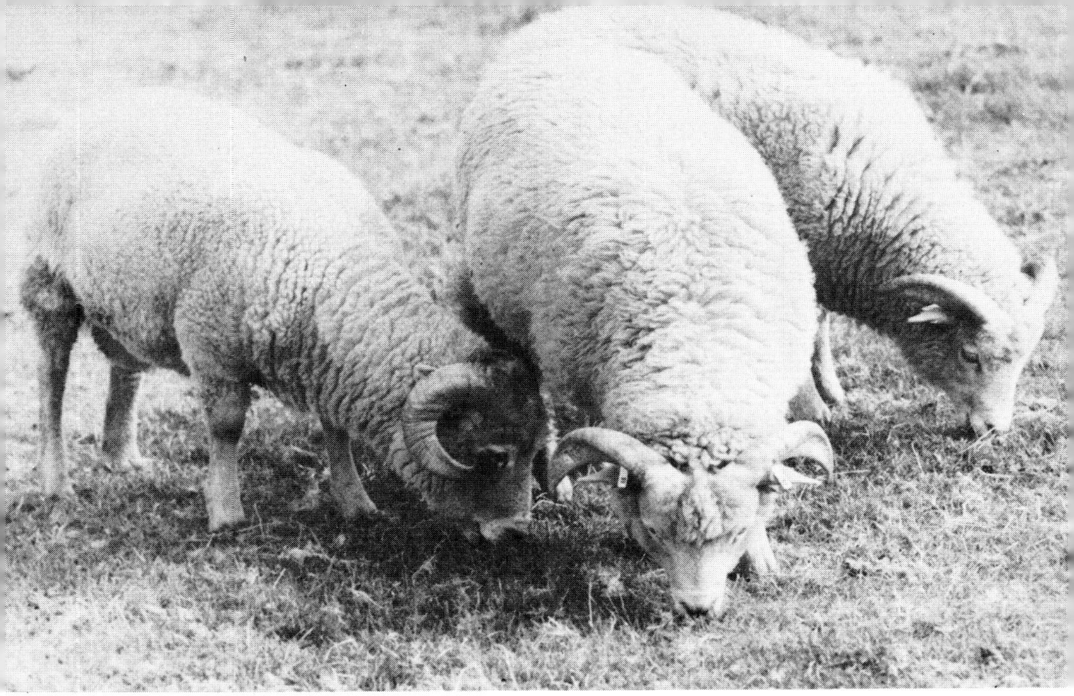

ABOVE: *Portland sheep, like many continental breeds, can lamb at any time of year.*

BELOW LEFT: *Southdown sheep —a nineteenth-century engraving.*
BELOW RIGHT: *A nineteenth-century engraving of a Hampshire Down sheep.*

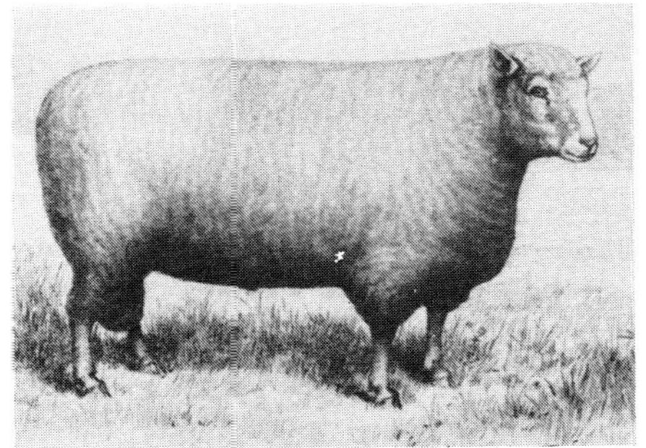

LONG WOOLLED BREEDS

LEICESTER: Once the most extensively distributed breed in Britain, it has several distinct strains, including the Wensleydale or the Yorkshire Leicester, the Dishley or Bakewell's Improved Variety, and the Teeswater. Late in the last century Leicesters were to be found in the lowland part of Northumberland, in Cumberland and southern part of Yorkshire, on the downs of the Midlands, in Cheshire and in south Lancashire. Sheep of the Teeswater strain were called 'mugs'.

BORDER LEICESTER: Developed from the Leicesters and recognised as a distinct breed in 1860. The rams were particularly prized as they

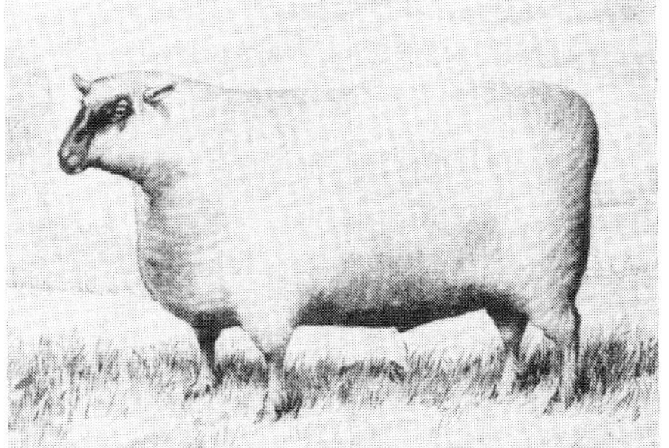

were used in cross breeding with Cheviots to produce Half-Breds; and with Blackfaces to produce Cross-Breds.

YORKSHIRE LEICESTER OR WENSLEYDALE: In south Yorkshire and Lincoln this breed was also known as Mashams. They were reputed to yield a high proportion of twin lambs. The breed was developed from the Teeswater strain.

LINCOLNS: These were renowned for the great weight of their wool — a single fleece could reach 30 lbs. They are the largest sheep among the British breeds. In the last century, flocks were mostly to be found on Lincoln Heath and in the Wolds.

COTSWOLDS: These are probably descended from the sheep introduced in Roman times, and were responsible for much of the prosperity enjoyed in the Cotswolds during the Middle Ages. Cotswold market towns still bear the unmistakable marks of the wealth generated by the wool trade in the shape of their fine churches and merchants' houses. Numerous brass memorials showing merchants and their wives also bear woolsacks and sometimes a representation of a sheep. At Northleach, Glos, one brass combines a woolsack, a sheep and a shepherd's crook in a single design. The Cotswold sheep is very similar in appearance to the Leicester.

DEVON LONGWOOLS: This local breed is found in the valleys of Devon and Somerset. The Devon South Ham strain was similar to the Romney Marsh breed and was favoured in the Vale of Honiton and along the lower valleys in Cornwall. The breed was improved by the addition of Leicester blood. Its origin was the Bampton Notts ('Nott' meaning polled) which had been in Devon for centuries. In 1808 they were able to provide fleeces weighing 6½ lbs. The name Devon Longwools seems to have been adopted a century or so ago and the flock book was started in 1889.

ROMNEY MARSH OR KENTISH: This breed, which had its natural home on the Kent marshes, was improved by the addition of Leicester blood and gradually spread its influence to other counties. Numerically, it is the most important of our long woolled breeds.

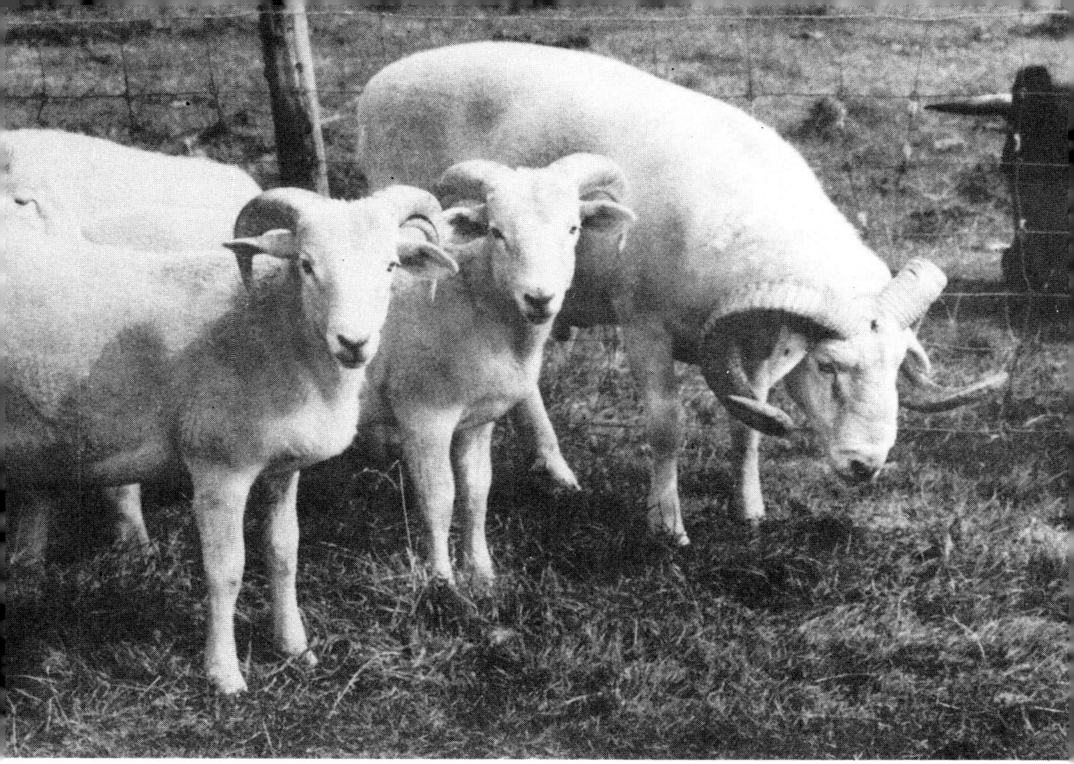

OPPOSITE: *The Somerset and Dorset Horned breed is an amalgam of Portland sheep and Southdowns.*
ABOVE: *Wiltshire Horn rams are used for cross-breeding to produce early fat lambs.*
BELOW: *Oxford Down sheep and lambs.*

SHORT WOOLLED BREEDS

OXFORD DOWNS: The breed was developed in the reign of William IV by crossing Southdowns or Hampshires with Cotswolds. One Victorian observer indicates that Leicester blood was also introduced. The success of the breed shows us just how well developed the techniques were in those early days. For many years the breed lacked a precise name and at one stage they were called Down Cotswolds. In 1857 the title Oxfordshire Downs was adopted and this was later shortened to the title we use today. The Flock Book began in 1889. The breed is particularly interesting as it amalgamates two distinct types of sheep i.e. the longwool and the shortwool. The Oxford Down is the heaviest of the Downland breeds.

SUFFOLK DOWNS: This heavy breed probably inherited some characteristics from

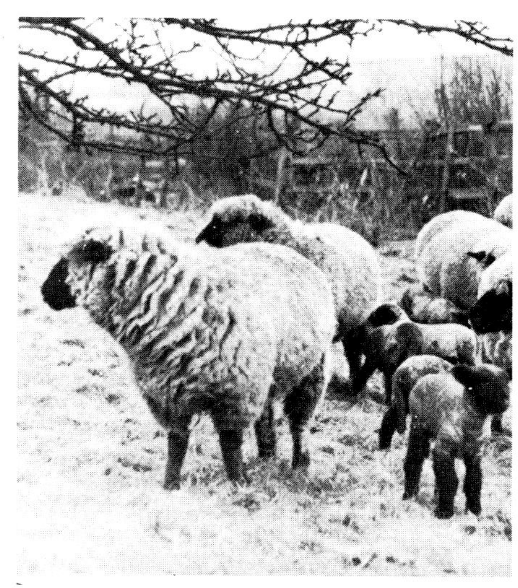

the ancient flocks of Norfolk. Suffolks have a reputation for bearing twin lambs.

SOUTHDOWN OR SUSSEX: Sheep have been bred on the chalk hills of the South Downs from very ancient times. Gilbert White of Selborne provides us with one of the earliest detailed accounts of the sheep to be found there. In 1773 he recorded an interesting observation concerning the sheep of his district. He noticed that all the sheep to the west of the river Adur had horns and white faces. To the east of that river the flocks were composed of polled sheep with black faces. He reported that 'an intelligent friend' of his had decided to experiment by crossing some polled and specked legged rams with horned ewes. The breeder who is usually credited with the origin of the Southdowns was John Ellman of Glynde, Sussex. In 1788 Arthur Young also noticed the effects of John Ellman's efforts and was clearly impressed by the fact that three Southdowns could exist happily on land which could scarcely support a single sheep of another breed. John Ellman visited Thomas Coke of Holkham and in 1791 five hundred Southdowns were sent there. The breed's popularity endured during the nineteenth century and influenced many parts of the country, except the wet regions and northern parts. It was widely exported. Southdowns made their way to France as early as 1827 and later to Canada, New Zealand, Australia and the U.S.A.

HAMPSHIRE DOWNS: The breed probably derived from the crossing of the Wiltshire white faced horned breed and the 'Berkshire Knot' with Southdown blood. It was common in the south of England during the last century.

PORTLANDS: These animals seem to have arrived by accident on the Isle of Portland having survived a shipwreck. One tradition suggests that the wreck formed part of the Spanish Armada. In common with many Continental breeds these sheep can lamb at any time of the year. Portlands are nearing extinction. There is a flock of forty at Calk Abbey, Derbyshire where the breed has been reared for two centuries. It disappeared from the Isle in the early years of this century but a flock has now been re-established there. Portland lamb was a delicacy enjoyed by George II when he visited Weymouth at Christmas time.

SOMERSET AND DORSET HORNED: This white-faced breed is an amalgam of Portlands and Southdowns. The horns of the ram are very convoluted. One great advantage of this breed is the capacity of the ewes to bear two lambs in one year. During the last century the breed penetrated the Forest of Dean and the Mendips.

WILTSHIRE HORN: The name comes from its county of origin. This breed bears the lightest wool to be found among British flocks. Wilt-

OPPOSITE: *A Victorian engraving of a Black-faced ram, a hardy breed from the Border Country.*
ABOVE: *St Kilda sheep were probably in-troduced by the Vikings to the remote island from which they are named.*
BELOW: *Moorit Shetland sheep. 'Moorit' is Gaelic for 'moor red'.*

shire rams are often used for cross-breeding when the object is to produce early fat lambs. Wiltshire Horns have strayed far from their native county, where they are seldom seen, to Northamptonshire and Buckinghamshire.

SHROPSHIRE DOWN: The breed arose from crossing the original Morfe Common breed with Leicesters, Cotswolds and then with Southdowns. Primrose McConnell suggested that blood from the Cannock Heath breed was also present. Shropshires are, in appearance, larger versions of the Southdowns.

RYELANDS: This small breed thrived in the area of that name in Herefordshire. Rams and ewes had a tuft of wool on the forehead. They were once prized for the quality of their meat. In the last century they had spread into Shropshire, Monmouth, Gloucester and Warwick. There were particular names for these other local strains — e.g. Ross, Ar-cherfield, Hereford, Dean-Forest, Malvern and Leominster (Lempster).

JACOB SHEEP: These came to England in the seventeenth century from Spain, which is why they are also called Spanish Sheep. The spotted nature of their coats makes them less suited for commercial use. Their value as ornamental creatures is obvious and it is this quality which has enabled them to survive in such numbers — there are some three thousand in more than a hundred different flocks. The Jacob Sheep Society was formed in 1969.

BELOW: *Soay sheep are descended from the prehistoric flocks first domesticated.*
OPPOSITE: *An Orkney sheep, a breed which often produces twin lambs and in Orkney thrives on seaweed from the beaches.*

MOUNTAIN BREEDS

BLACKFACED: Like most other breeds its origins are lost. It belongs to the high hills bordering England and Scotland and has a well-deserved reputation for hardiness. The breed has been crossed with Leicesters to give 'Crossbreds' or 'Grey Faces'. Other old names for this breed include Blackfaced Heath, Linton, Short and Forest. Today the Blackface is one of the most common breeds to be found. Flocks can be seen on the Scottish moors, along the Pennines, on Dartmoor and even in Cornwall.

CHEVIOTS: This breed originated in Northumberland and was later introduced into the Border counties. Like the Blackfaced, the Cheviots could endure the harsh climate of the hills. Not all the rams were horned.

ISLAND BREEDS

SHETLAND: Originally small in size in relation to their mainland counterparts, they have an almost goat-like appearance with their back-ward curving horns and range in colour from white to brown and black. Their fleece is mixed with hair and for this reason it is not clipped but is pulled off when it separates in the summer. The improved modern breed has been changed in stature as it contains Cheviot and Border Leicester blood. This means that the pure Shetland may become very reduced in numbers. The wool has formed the basis of the famous Shetland and Fair Isle knitting industry.

MOORIT SHETLAND: This breed gives us a glimpse of the native breeds which were found in many parts of the northern hemisphere during ancient times. The colour of the fleece gives them the name we use today: 'moorit' is Gaelic for 'moor red'.

ST KILDA: This breed probably came to the remoteness of the North Atlantic with the Vikings more than a thousand years ago. None remains on St Kilda but there are about 250 in zoos and private parks. They can have two, four or even six horns. The fleece is black but becomes silvery grey with age.

SOAY: The two-horned Soays are a fine example of living history. They represent the last survivors of those prehistoric European flocks which were probably the very first to be domesticated. Neolithic graves have revealed the bones of sheep very similar to those of today's Soays. The breed has a very special genetic importance: in relation to their size they bear the largest lambs. Soays still exist in the St Kilda group of islands but should not be confused with the multi-horned St Kilda breed. The flock at the Cotswold Farm Park came from the island of Hirta.

MANX LOGHTAN: It seems probable that the Vikings were responsible for the introduction of this breed to the Isle of Man. The name comes from two Manx words 'lugh' (mouse) and 'dhoan' (brown) which describes the colours found in the fleece. The breed is the largest of the moorits and the rams have four or six horns. A flock of twenty-five ewes can be seen at the Manx Museum at Cregneash but the breed has diminished to very small proportions — there are less than a hundred survivors. The Cotswold Farm Park is working in conjunction with the Royal Agricultural Society in an effort to increase their numbers.

ORKNEY: This is another breed which probably owes its presence to the Vikings. In their native habitat they exist mostly on seaweed and have been called the seaweed eaters. They have a very hardy constitution, to be expected from a breed which has for generations been confined to the seashore. Orkneys often produce twin lambs or even triplets. The rams are horned but the ewes are usually polled (hornless).

So varied are the breeds of British sheep that there is not enough space here to detail them all. Their often fascinating names however deserve an honourable mention.

The Swaledale, found in the northern Pennines, is a larger version of the Blackfaced.

The Rough Fell is a local breed found to the south and west of the Swaledale territory.

Another native of the Pennines is the Dales Breed. Its black face is distinguished by the white mark on each side of the nostrils. Both rams and ewes are horned.

Lonks occupy the Pennines too, and are found on the western fringe of Yorkshire and in east Lancashire. They have more white on the face than the Dales.

Derbyshire Gritstones can be found mostly in the north-west of that county. They are larger than the Blackfaces and their faces and legs are black with white markings.

The Limestones and the Penistone breeds were another purely local type so often found a century or so ago. In 1966 they were said to be virtually extinct and the author would be pleased to know that this is not so.

Herdwicks still roam the Lake District. The rams may be horned or polled. The dark faces of the lambs change to grey then to white as they reach maturity.

Exmoor Horns have a stocky look and carry a very thick fleece. They can also be found eastwards of Exmoor where the ewes are often crossed with other breeds.

OPPOSITE: *Manx Loghtans — less than a hundred of this breed now survive.*
BELOW: *A Jacob ewe. This breed owes its survival to its decorative appearance.*

Welsh Mountain sheep are descended from the tan-faced breeds of the Celts. Unlike some other breeds they scramble through obstacles instead of jumping over them.

Another Welsh breed is the Kerry Hill, noted for its variations which depend largely upon the habitat (upland or lowland) in which flocks are reared.

Radnor Forest sheep are confined to a relatively small geographical area. Their characteristics are similar to the Welsh Mountain and the Kerry Hill.

Clun Forest sheep have dark faces and dark legs. Since the 1940s the breed has found favour in many parts of the British Isles.

Llanwenog sheep are very similar to Cluns and have become a recognised breed in recent years.

The North Country Cheviot originated in Sutherland and Caithness but its flocks have spread into the south-east corner of Scotland. North Country sheep are larger than Cheviots and their ears are not so erect. They have white faces.

SWINE

Pigs were domesticated in prehistoric times but the wild boar is still found in parts of Europe and was hunted in England in medieval times. Among the woodlands both the domestic and wild swine foraged for acorns and beech nuts. The cottagers of Victorian Britain depended upon the family pig which was often partly mortgaged to the miller, the boot maker and other tradesmen before it was killed. Many writers have provided us with detailed accounts of the pig's last hour. Thomas Hardy (*Jude the Obscure*) notes that the stuck pig should be 'eight or ten minutes dying at least'. After the killing came the scalding and the scraping. Later on when the carcass was hung in the

pantry it was suspended from the large hook fixed to a beam in the ceiling. Flora Thompson (*Lark Rise to Candleford*) relates how young Laura crept into the 'cold silence' of the pantry to converse with the pig she had known all its life. In those days the pig was an essential part of the farm worker's budget.

There are many country words connected with pigs, which have mostly gone out of use. A barrow-pig was the name widely used for a castrated boar. An alternative name for a boar was brawn. In Kent a spayed sow was known as a yolk. The smallest pig in a litter had various names — runt, dilling and (in Roxburgh) a krute. A half grown sow was called a shot. The common names for a sow were hilt, gelt and yilt (Essex). There were several names for a pig sty, often called a hobble in East Anglia. To prevent a pig from breaking out of a fence a primitive yoke called a yangle was placed around its neck. The man responsible for feeding the pigs was known in Hampshire as a fogger.

In the eighteenth century there were numerous local breeds of pigs, all of which seem to have been very large and to have produced inferior meat. The family tree of our British breeds is impossible to chronicle but we do know that the native strains were improved by importations from China and Italy. The immense size of the old English pigs was recorded in 1807 in Culley's 'Observations on Live Stock'. He provides us with the details of a Cheshire pig slaughtered on 24th January 1774. It measured from nose to tail 9 feet 8 inches and stood 4 feet 5½ inches high. Alive its weight was 12 cwt. 66 lbs. and when dressed the carcass was 10 cwt. 95 lbs. The principal local breeds in the 1850s were the Old Lincolnshire, the Prick-eared, the Sussex and Kentish, the Cheshire, the Shropshire, the Hampshire, the Gloucester, the Wiltshire and the Herefordshire. There were, no doubt, many other types resulting from cross breeding. The more important breeds were the Berkshire and the Essex. Different agricultural writers adopted different names for the same breed, and this makes old books on livestock somewhat confusing.

Changing demands in public tastes had a considerable influence on livestock breeders. New breeds were developed to meet the needs of the butchers and by the 1900s many of the ancient strains had disappeared. Pigs developed a new look, with longer heads and less bulky bodies.

ABOVE: *A Large Black sow.*

LEFT: *A Middle White.*

BERKSHIRE: This was one of the first breeds to attract the attention of the breeders. Early in the nineteenth century the characteristic colour was black with white or sandy spots. As the breed evolved the white patches were confined to the forehead and the lower part of the legs.

LARGE WHITE: The breed represents a mixture which derives from Chinese, Neapolitan, Berkshire and Essex strains. Large Whites are also known as Yorkshires. The Middle and Small White breeds shared some characteristics of the larger one but were chiefly distinguished by their size.

TAMWORTH: An ancient breed with a distinctive red (brown) coat and, sometimes, black spots. In 1973 a Tamworth sow at the Cotswold Farm Park produced a litter fathered by a wild boar. The resultant striped piglets were bred specifically to be reared at the reconstructed Iron Age village at Butser Hill, Hampshire.

LARGE BLACK: There were two main variations within this breed. One was found in the west where Cornish miners are said to have preferred fatter pork. The other leaner strain was to be found in East Anglia.

GLOUCESTER OLD SPOT: An attractive breed well marked with black spots. Gloucesters were also called 'orchard pigs' as they could happily survive on windfalls and required the minimum of expense or attention. They are a hardy outdoor breed renowned for large litters.